GrowthSpurt

Also by Jerry Scott and Jim Borgman

Zits: Sketchbook 1

GrowthSpurt

Zits®

Sketchbook 2

by JERRY SCOTT and JIM BORGMAN

**Andrews McMeel
Publishing, LLC**

Kansas City

──────── **ATTENTION: SCHOOLS AND BUSINESSES** ────────

Andrews McMeel books are available at quantity discounts with bulk purchase for educational, business, or sales promotional use. For information, please write to: Special Sales Department, Andrews McMeel Publishing, LLC, 1130 Walnut Street, Kansas City, Missouri 64106

To Kim and Lynn

12

17

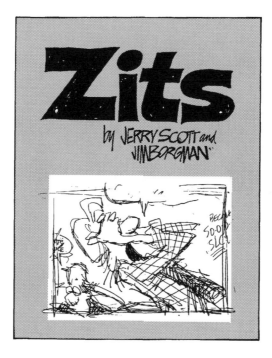

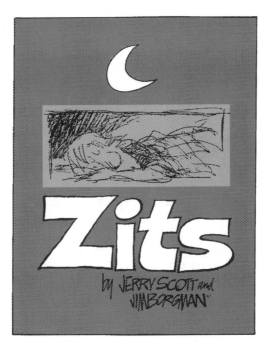

31

33

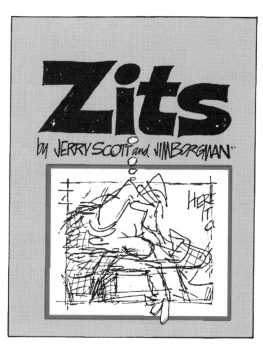

40

48

49

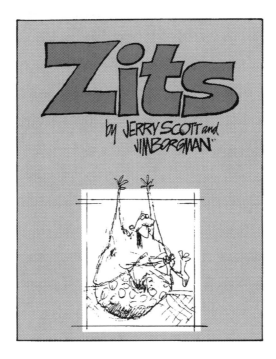

51

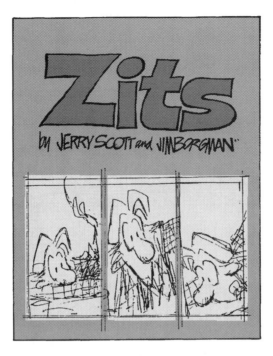

63

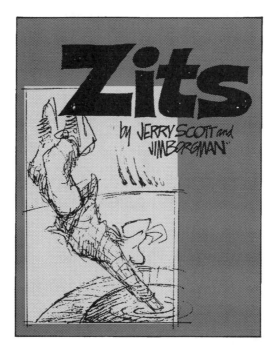

67

68

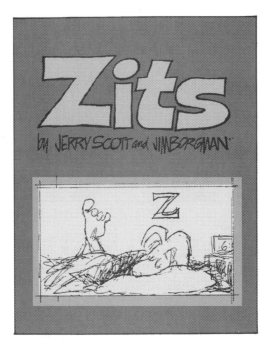

76

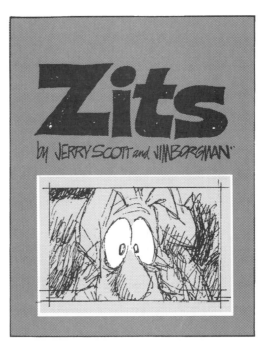

92

94

97

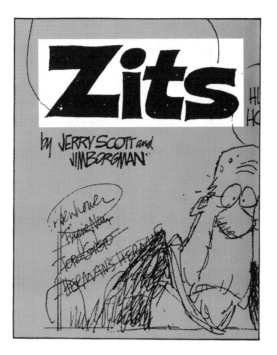

I'VE GOT MY FOLKS REALLY CONCERNED ABOUT ME SINCE I PAINTED MY ROOM BLACK AND STARTED WEARING THIS DOG COLLAR.

HM

AND I'VE DROPPED A HINT OR TWO THAT A NEW COMPUTER JUST MIGHT KEEP ME FROM GOING FURTHER ASTRAY.

NOW ALL I HAVE TO DO IS BIDE MY TIME UNTIL I SEE EXACTLY WHAT I'LL BE GETTING.

SCOTT and BORGMAN

MORE "FAMILY" TIME

AND LOTS OF HUGS!

JEREMY, CAN WE TALK TO YOU?

SURE. JUST LET ME TURN DOWN THE VOLUME ON THIS DISTURBING HEAVY-METAL MUSIC.

HERE IT COMES!

YOUR FATHER AND I HAVE DECIDED TO GIVE YOU A VERY VALUABLE GIFT.

YES! YES! I KNEW IT!

OUR TIME.

SCOTT and BORGMAN

AND...?

LOTS OF HUGS! ANYTIME YOU WANT 'EM!

SO YOU'RE NOT GOING TO BUY ME A NEW COMPUTER?

NO

YOU MEAN YOU'RE NOT WORRIED ABOUT ME? COME ON! I PAINTED MY ROOM **BLACK** AND I'M WEARING A **DOG COLLAR!** IF THAT ISN'T A CRY FOR HELP, I DON'T KNOW WHAT IS!

AND THAT'S WHY WE DECIDED TO START SPENDING EVEN MORE TIME WITH YOU.

LET'S RAP!

SCOTT and BORGMAN

BACKFIRED, HUH?

SHUT UP AND GRAB A PAINT BRUSH!

WHITE

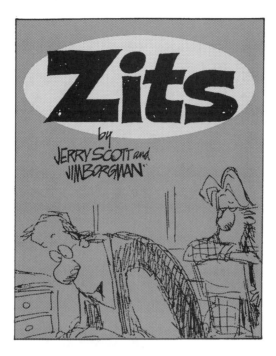

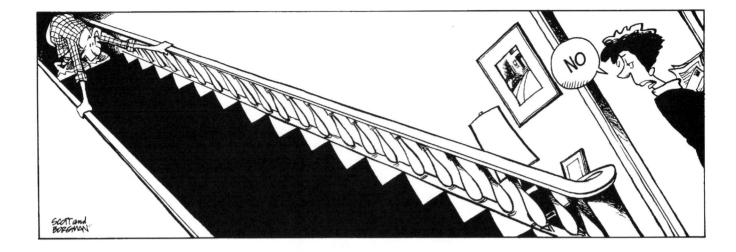

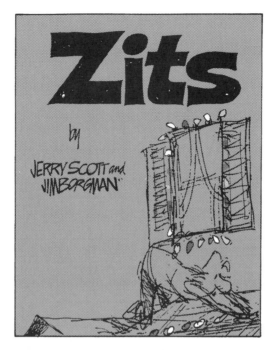

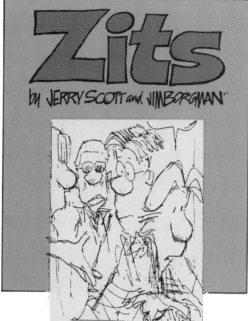

116

117

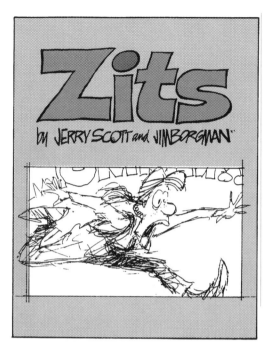

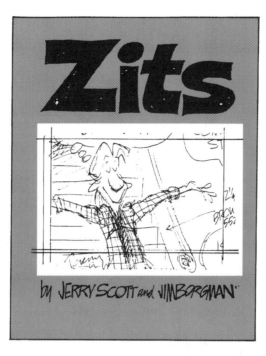

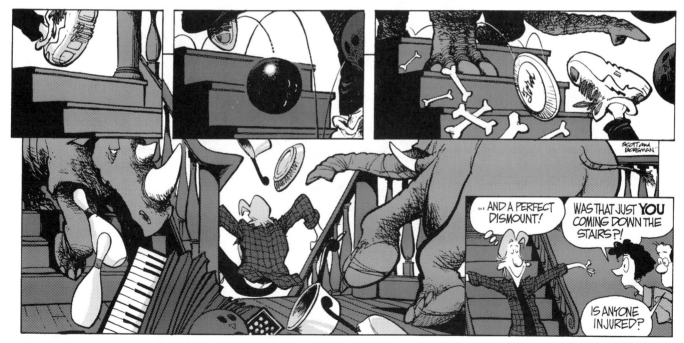

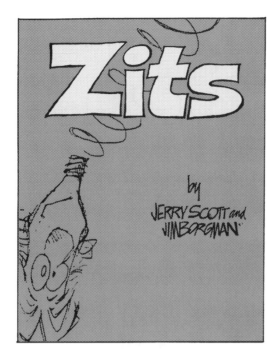

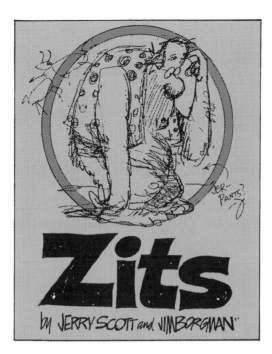